Contents

*C = copper; B = bronze; S = silver; T = teacher; ( ) = the line must be played but cannot be assessed for a Medal.

Stamp Your Feet!

Trad. Czech. arr. Kathy and David Blackwell

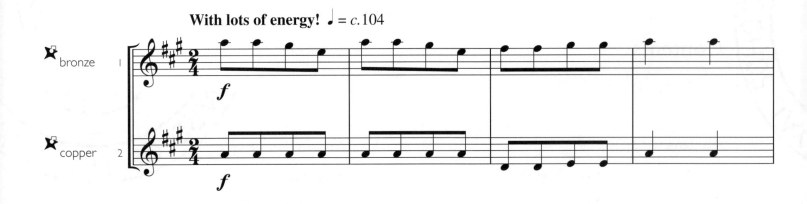

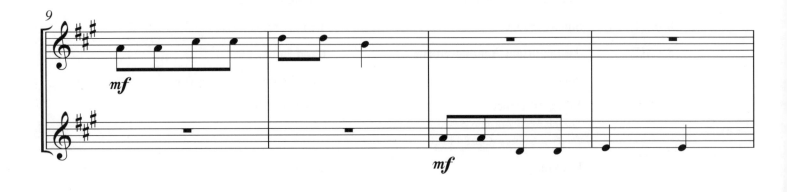

AB 3015

Stick in the Mud

Edward Huws Jones

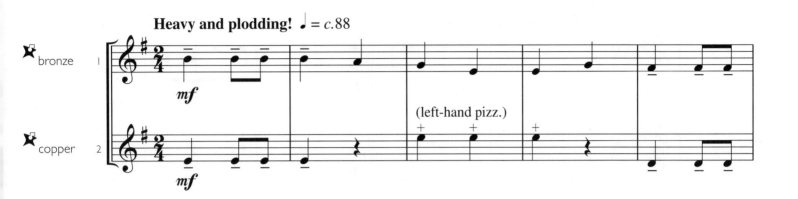

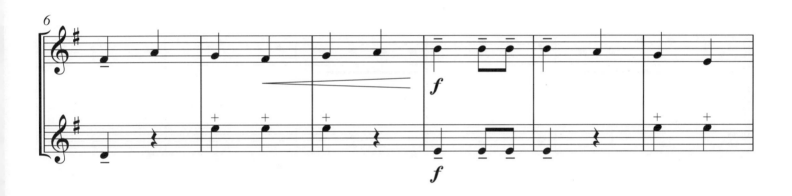

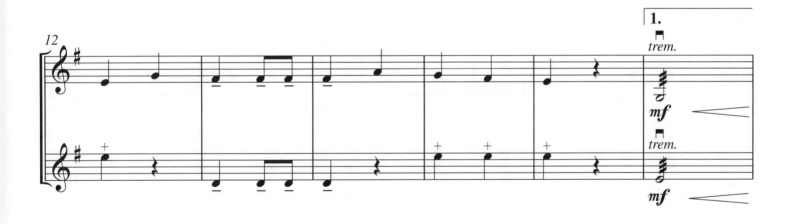

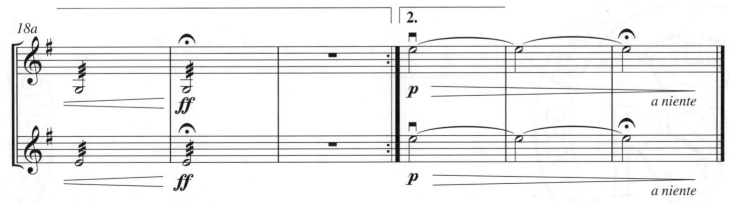

Red Hot Chilli Peppers

Mary Cohen

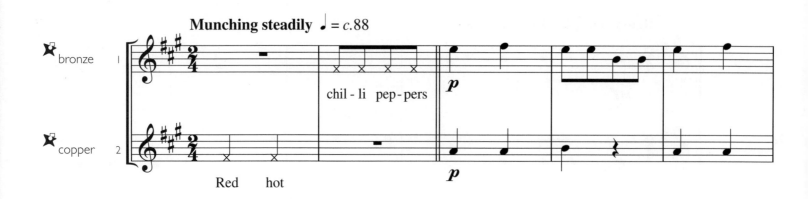

AB 3015

Saturday Strut

Kathy and David Blackwell

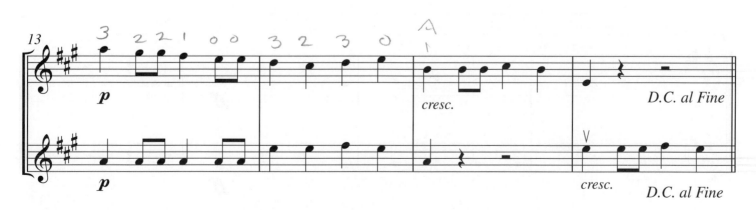

Watch Out! Something's Coming...

Katherine and Hugh Colledge

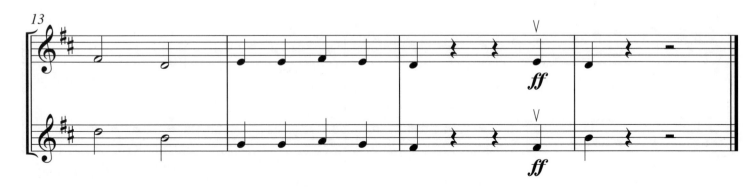

Melting Icicles

Mary Cohen

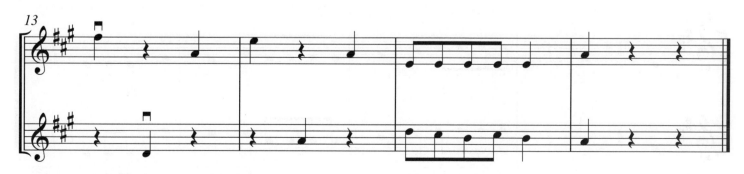

Let's Go!

Katherine and Hugh Colledge

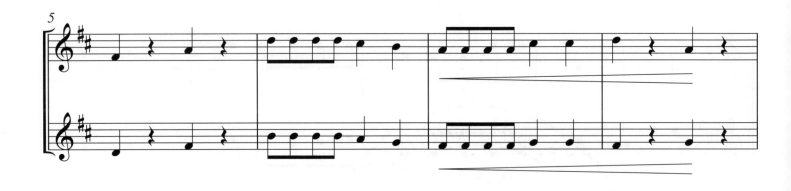

AB 3015

Eating Spaghetti with a Spoon and Fork

Katie Wearing

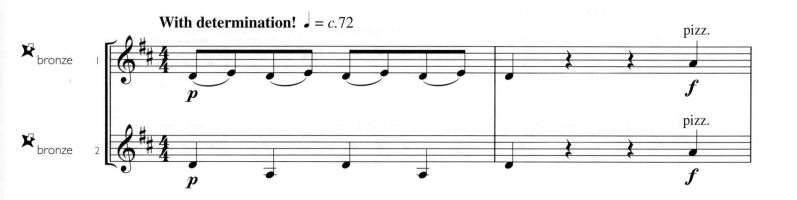

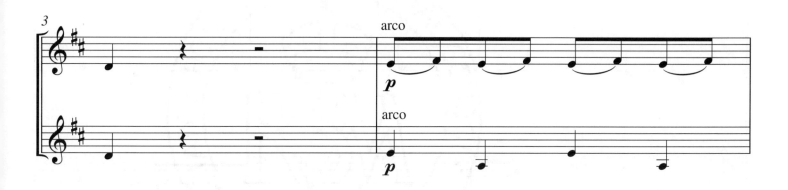

Riding in Tandem

David Stone

AB 3015

Swingsong

Sheila Nelson

I'm a Little Monkey

Polly Waterfield

AB 3015

Summertime on Brownstone Street

Anthony Marks

AB 3015

A Good Argument

Polly Waterfield

AB 3015

Mary Denton's Pavan

Edward Huws Jones

Square Dance

Trad. arr. Kathy and David Blackwell

Loud and fast! ♩ = *c.*120

AB 3015

An Important Announcement

David Stone

Fais dodo

Trad. French arr. Anthony Marks

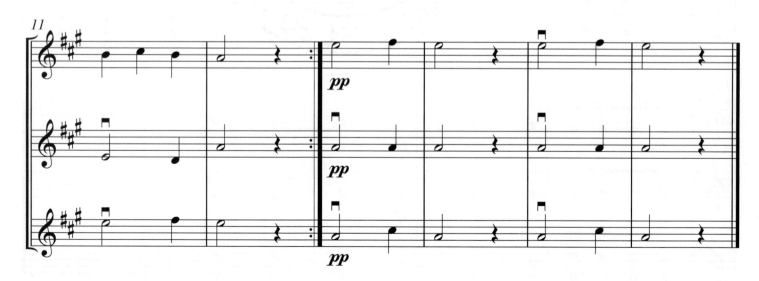

Fais dodo is a lullaby. The title means 'Go to sleep'.

AB 3015

Villagers' Dance

Theme from 'Autumn' from *The Four Seasons*, Op. 8 No. 3

Vivaldi arr. Mary Cohen

Dreaming

Christine Myers

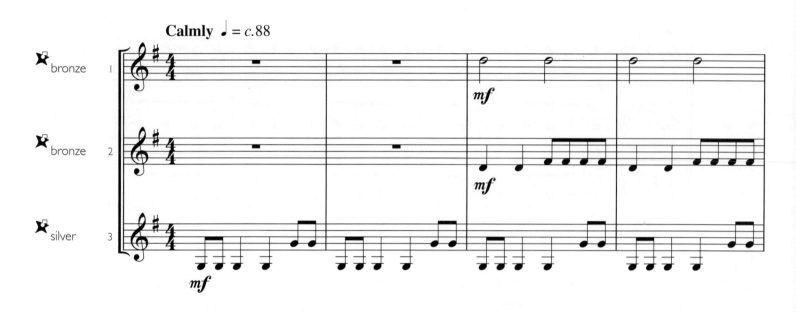

AB 3015

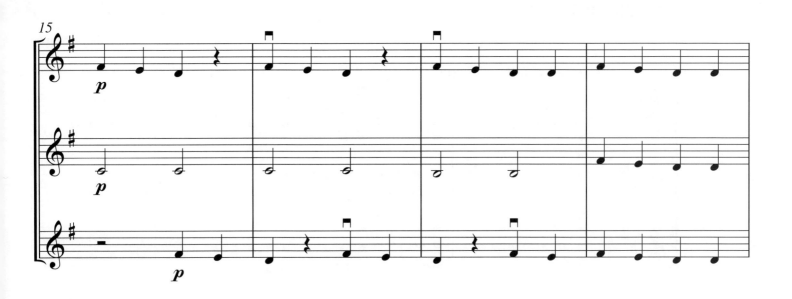

Frogs' Fancy

Sheila Nelson

On Alert!

Mary Cohen

Who's There?

Sheila Nelson

AB 3015